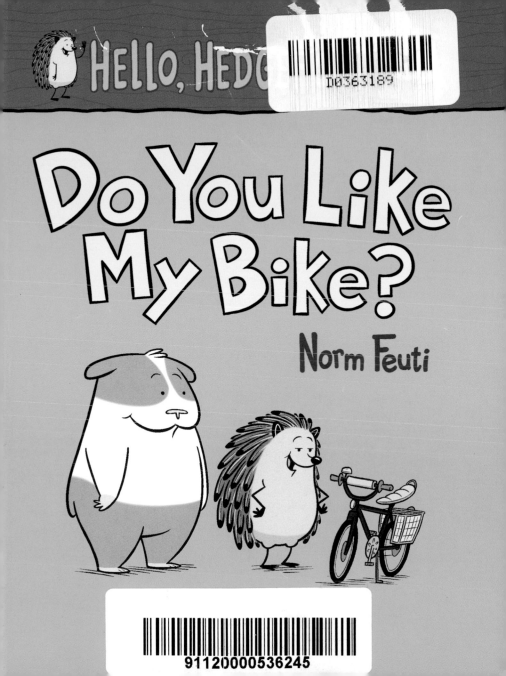

HELLO, HEDG

Do You Like My Bike?

Norm Feuti

For Mom – NF

Published in the UK by Scholastic, 2022
Euston House, 24 Eversholt Street, London, NW1 1DB
Scholastic Ireland, 89E Lagan Road, Dublin Industrial Estate, Glasnevin, Dublin, D11 HP5F

SCHOLASTIC and associated logos are trademarks and/or
registered trademarks of Scholastic Inc.

First published in the US by Scholastic Inc, 2019

Text and illustrations © Norm Feuti, 2019

The right of Norm Feuti to be identified as the author and illustrator of this work has been asserted by him
under the Copyright, Designs and Patents Act 1988.

ISBN 978 0702 30083 7

A CIP catalogue record for this book is available from the British Library.

Printed in China
Paper made from wood grown in sustainable forests and other controlled sources.

1 3 5 7 9 10 8 6 4 2

This is a work of fiction. Names, characters, places, incidents and dialogues are products of the author's
imagination or are used fictitiously. Any resemblance to actual people, living or dead, events or locales is
entirely coincidental.

www.scholastic.co.uk

Edited by Katie Carella
Book design by Maria Mercado

4

5

6

8

14

22

23

28

29

30

34

37

41

43

About the Author

Norm Feuti lives in Massachusetts, USA with his family, a dog, two cats and a guinea pig. He is the creator of the newspaper comic strips **Retail** and **Gil**. He is also the author and illustrator of the graphic novel **The King of Kazoo**. **Hello, Hedgehog!** is Norm's first early reader series.

YOU CAN DRAW HEDGEHOG!

1. Draw a jelly bean shape.

2. Draw the nose and eyes.

3. Add ears and lots of quills!

4. Draw little arms and hands. Add legs and feet, too!

5. Put black spots on the ends of the quills. Finish the face.

6. Colour in your drawing!

WHAT'S YOUR STORY?

Hedgehog goes bike riding with Harry.
Imagine Hedgehog asks **you** to go bike riding.
What would your bike look like?
Where would you and Hedgehog go?
Write and draw your story!

HIH

Books should be returned or renewed by the last
date above. Renew by phone **03000 41 31 31** or
online *www.kent.gov.uk/libs*

Libraries Registration & Archives

POPE
FRANCIS

BY EMANUEL CASTRO   ILLUSTRATED BY IGNACIO SEGESSO

Raintree is an imprint of Capstone Global Library Limited,
a company incorporated in England and Wales having its
registered office at 264 Banbury Road, Oxford, OX2 7DY
– Registered company number: 6695582

www.raintree.co.uk
myorders@raintree.co.uk

ISBN 978 1 4747 5142 1 (paperback)
21 20 19 18 17
10 9 8 7 6 5 4 3 2 1

By Emanuel Castro
Illustrated by Ignacio Segesso

British Library Cataloguing in Publication Data
A full catalogue record for this book is available from the
British Library.

Translated into the English language by Trusted
Translations

Printed and bound in China.

CONTENTS

No one will ever know the words that were whispered in Pope Francis' ear. But through his story some answers appear clear. It starts at the Church of Saint Francis of Assisi in Turin, Italy, in the year 1841.

This is unthinkable in this church! When you are ordered to pray, pray; when you are ordered to confess, confess!

Ah, Father! You're hurting me! Ouch!

It's ok, Father. I'll take care of him.

Why was the sexton yelling at you, boy?

Tell me, have you taken communion?

Because I don't know how to be an acolyte.

No, Father. I don't know the catechism, either. I'm poor. My parents left me.

5

This man was Don Bosco, and the boy, named Bartholomew Garelli, showed him the harsh reality of childhood in Italy.

Five years later, Don Bosco started his "Oratory," a workshop where he rescued 400 children from factories and prisons to teach them trades with which they would be able to earn a living.

Don Bosco's dream had become a reality. Thousands of children went through his Oratory, where they were educated and fed. But for him, that wasn't enough. He had to do more.

After founding his own order, called the "Society of St Francis de Sales," he sent his brothers on missions throughout Europe and eventually beyond. Argentina would be the first American country the "Salesians" would reach, in 1875.

They founded the Basilica of San Carlos Borromeo and María Auxiliadora right in the neighbourhood of Almagro, Buenos Aires.

Very good. The carrots have to be thinly sliced. Have you put the ossobuco in yet? That has to go first, because it takes longer to cook.

When he was a child, Jorge Mario had to help out at home because of his mother's temporary injury.

Yes, Mum. Can't you tell how good it smells?

The salt. Don't forget the salt. That has to go in first.

Hello!

Very good! That's what I like to see, you boys helping your mother.

You know what, Uncle? I can do it by myself. The other day, I made the meal. It was delicious.

Perfect! That reminds me of a naughty little song from Genoa that says...

Be quiet!

So what? They're in italian. Who's going to understand them?

Don't sing them those songs. They'll repeat them at school!

8

12

13

It wasn't a big job. Neither was the wage. But it was money. And Jorge felt like the happiest person in the world because he was able to make a living on his own.

But once summer holidays were over, he had to pass the high school entrance exam. He spent any hour he wasn't working studying.

The day finally arrived. He tested for a technical school that specialized in chemistry.

I passed!

15

CHAPTER 2
BETWEEN LIFE
AND DEATH

One year before finishing high school, Jorge Bergoglio decided to try his luck at another job.

It's a pleasure to meet you, Jorge. Come, sit down.

17

19

One day, when he was 21 years old, Jorge woke up feeling ill.

You have a 39 degree fever. We have to call the doctor.

No, Mum. If I take an aspirin, I'll be fine tomorrow.

But he didn't get better, and he ended up in the hospital.

He has pneumonia, but we should be able to get it under control soon enough. But there's something else that's more serious.

The x-rays have found three lumps on his right lung. As soon as the pneumonia calms down, we're going to have to remove them.

21

Jorge wasn't the first person to make this connection. In the year 1521 in Spain, soldier Ignatius of Loyola returned from war with injuries that left both of his legs broken.

While he rested, he studied the life of Christ.

Pain ... what does it mean? Christ suffered as well...

That vision ended up convincing him to hang up his military uniform. He dressed in rags and hid out in a cave in the Manresa mountains of Spain, where he wrote his "Spiritual Exercises."

Ignatius, I am your Mother, the Mother of Christ... Your pain hurts me as well ... and the pain of war... Leave it behind, Ignacio... You can do something to help mitigate the world's pain...

But it wouldn't be until later at the University of Paris, where he studied philosophy, that he would obtain his first followers by inviting them to read his "Exercises."

And on 15 August 1534...

We promise to serve Our Lord, leaving behind all earthly things.

When the Pope heard them in Rome, he understood the truth of the mission.

Yes, my sons, I give you my blessing to establish your religious order...

We have a very important mission to accomplish. A mission that will go beyond our lives. To travel throughout the world, founding schools and universities.

Within two centuries, the "Jesuits", the term we now use to refer to the "Society of Jesus", would go on missions to Argentina, teaching reading, arts, trades and Christianity to the people there.

The works of art from that period remind us of the strength of the Jesuit brothers.

And the schools they established are evidence of their commitment to education.

CHAPTER 3

THE CALLING

When Jorge Bergoglio was 17 years old, and it was the first day of spring.

Bye, Mum!

Have fun!

27

I don't know. I just saw the church and felt like confessing.

No one knows what he told the priest that morning. Confessions are kept private.

What we do know is that he felt amazed. Amazed that he had found someone who was waiting for him. Jorge was looking for God, but God found him first.

He never did go to the station to meet up with his friends from school; rather, he went back home. He knew that he had felt God and that there was no going back.

For three years, he was forced to keep his calling quiet. This can be something that's hard for a young person's parents to understand.

Jorge, you've seemed quite depressed lately. Are you ill? Is something going on?

Yes, Dad. I can't hide it anymore. Something is going on, but it's not an illness.

What?

I want to be a priest.

Do you think it's a bad idea?

No! I think it's great, and I'm very happy for you!

29

30

A short time later, Jorge Bergoglio entered the Minor Seminary of Villa Devoto.

But that didn't mean that he would become distanced from his family.

Dad! You came to visit!

What about mum? Why didn't she come?

Well ... She ... She's still working through your decision...

Leave her to me. I'm going to fix this.

In 1958, when he was 21 years old, he made a huge leap to follow his second inspiration. He joined the Society of Jesus, founded by Ignatius of Loyola.

Now I know. I was drawn to this society due to its progressive take on the Church.

And above all, because of its importance for mission work.

He spent a decade studying classic sciences, history, literature, Latin and Greek.

Until 1969, when the big day arrived ... his ordination.

33

From that moment on, Jorge worked consistently as a priest and teacher at the Jesuit schools in Santa Fe and Buenos Aires, Argentina.

CHAPTER 4
THE TEACHER

Teacher Jorge knew that, and he also knew that once he got past his nerves, the student would do perfectly on the exam. He was happy to see that his thinking was right.

Well, my child, you have received an A+.

But we have to give you just an A. And that's not to scold you, but so that you'll always remember that the most important thing is fulfilling your daily obligations, carrying out everyday work.

You must build brick by brick, instead of in random bits that can seem so attractive. Study all year long, not just when you have an assignment.

37

I don't want to teach you all to memorize and repeat things, like parrots. And I don't expect you to learn everything, like a synopsis.

Let's see what "The Face" has for us today.

Shh! Give him a chance. It's the first class.

That's why I prefer to choose an author and an era for us to all study together. Today it will be "The Song of My Cid".

Teacher, I happen to have read "My Cid", but I've also read the poem by Machado, which is really great, and is inspired by the old song. Can I talk about that?

Go ahead.

Once he could tell that the students had an understanding of the readings and written exams, he happily challenged them.

Now, I'm going to give you all a test. Don't worry, it won't be graded. You'll have to do it at home over the next few weeks. The test will involve writing a story about any topic.

Obviously, some will be better than others. Not everyone has a knack for writing. but I promise that I'm going to read them all and select some to print.

THE face really had a great idea today! What if we end up being selected?

The Face, as his students called him because of his youthful appearance, really knew how to find their callings.

39

It was then that the years of the military dictatorship in Argentina arrived. Many people were tracked down, arrested and disappeared.

Father Jorge already had the most important position in the Jesuit order in the region. Thus, many people went to him for help.

Father, they're watching us because we work in poor areas. We're afraid.

CHAPTER 5
THE YEARS OF FIRE

43

What do you think?

Well, it fits me all right. Now we just have to see if it works.

Take this, it's my ID. You look quite a bit like me. Let's pray that they don't recognize you at the border.

Go on. Go through calmly. They'll surely ask you for ID. I'll watch you from here. And pray. Pray a lot.

It worked. Let us be thankful to God.

Years later, Jorge would be named Auxiliary Bishop of Buenos Aires. In that position, he was part of the group that went on spiritual retreats to an area outside of the capital city.

Yes, I still have some time before the train leaves.

CHAPTER 6
FROM BISHOP TO CARDINAL

As he did every day, he made his short trip to the cathedral. There, he felt relieved due to the silence and cool air compared to the sweltering summer's day.

But as he was heading out to go to the train station...

Father, please, I need to confess.

If I stay to hear his confession, I'm going to miss my train.

Another Father is on his way, and you can do your confession with him. I have somewhere to be.

That other Father is going to be a while, but I doubt the boy will notice, in his condition.

But what have I done? That young man needed me! My God, I feel so ashamed! I have to go back! I have to take his confession!

47

And so Pope John Paul II named him Cardinal under the title of Saint Robert Bellarmine.

From that moment on, his mission grew. It included the Congregation for Clergy, the Commission for Latin America, the Congregation for Divine Worship and the Discipline of the Sacraments. And, among others, the Argentine Episcopal Conference.

Even though his success grew, he still lived in a small flat where he cooked his own food.

I've got to eat quickly because San Lorenzo is playing tonight.

San Lorenzo, champion of the South American Cup!

Champions again!

50

With only a lung and a half, Jorge had the energy to watch over the poor, an endless number of commissions and spiritual retreats.

A blessing, Father!

I give you my blessing, little one. So that, when you grow up, you will be a good man.

It was during a speech at the parish of Our Lady of Caacupé in a settlement in the Buenos Aires neighbourhood of Barracas, where something emotional occurred.

Excuse me, Father, but I want to say that I am very proud of you...

51

... and I'm proud because when I was on my way here on the bus with my friend, I saw you sitting in one of the seats towards the back, just like anyone else. I told them, but they didn't believe me.

On 11 February 2013, far from Buenos Aires in the Vatican, Pope Benedict XVI made an explosive announcement.

I've come to the conclusion that, given my old age, I am not strong enough to continue as pope.

With total freedom, I declare that I leave the post of Bishop of Rome and successor of Saint Peter.

Days later, the Pope, now called "emeritus," left his duties for good when he flew to Castel Gandolfo, the summer home of the Pope, to dedicate himself to meditation. The church bells in Rome rang for him.

52

In the early 13th century, war devastated Italy. A young soldier named Francis, from Assisi, was tired of fighting.

CHAPTER 7
SO YOU WILL BE CALLED

His friends, his mother, they had all seen him turn moody as if something was troubling him.

This can't be the beautiful chapel of St Damian. What about its clergy and caretakers? Why have they let it break down like this?

That's when a miracle occurred...

Francis, fix my church that's falling to pieces.

Francis was the son of a rich fabric merchant.

My father already has enough money. He doesn't need these luxurious fabrics. On the other hand, St Damian does need their worth.

And after selling them...

This is a donation so that you can fix your church, Father.

We don't need your money here.

57

But I'm also giving up everything I own, recognizing God as my only father.

Oh, Francis. Today you have taught us all a lesson in humility. Let Our Lord bless you. I already have.

Just a few months later, he already had a group of disciples.

"Do not take a purse or bag or sandals, and do not greet anyone on the road." Luke, 10:4.

In 1209, Francis travelled to Rome to request the creation of an order of priests.

That was the beginning of the "Franciscan Order". He rebuilt churches and cared for lepers. Saint Francis influenced many men who travelled around the world to share his teachings.

I give you my blessing, Francis. Your humility and poverty will strengthen the image of the Church.

59

61

From 22–29 July 2013, Pope Francis attended the World Youth Days in Río de Janeiro, Brazil.

He's going to give me a heart attack. In addition to not using the armoured car, now he doesn't even want us near him.

Look at that. He's getting out of the car!

Another Pope may have been on the cover of *Time* magazine at some other point in time. But within such a short time of becoming Pope?

But even more unbelievable was the Pope being on the cover of a rock and roll magazine. It showed his huge popularity.

His second trip outside of Italy was to the Holy Land – Jordan, Palestine and Israel. There he met with the leaders of the region.

It is important that the State of Israel has the right to exist and enjoy peace. Just as the Palestinian people should be recognized as having a home country.

Building peace is difficult, but living without it is torture.

On 27 April 2014, he oversaw the ceremony honouring Popes John XXIII and John Paul II.

Later, he went to rest, while on the rooftop of the Vatican Prefecture for the Economic Affairs, business people and important figures enjoyed a dinner that cost £19,300.

What is this? £19,300?

It's from private investors, Your Holiness.

I don't care. I want a Church for the poor, and I have asked my priests to live frugally.

And on 13 August 2014, while Francis was on a trip to Korea...

Your Holiness! San Lorenzo just won the Libertadores Cup!

Wonderful! That's just what we needed!

Really? I'll have to tell him straight away!

This is Pope Francis. The American pope, the Argentine pope, the pope of the believers and the non-believers, everyone's pope.

He is not afraid to show his passion, or to go outside the norm. He has called on the Church to live plainly in these times of crisis. And he still has a lot left to do...

TIMELINE

1936–PRESENT

1936	1940s	1950s	1960s	1970s
Jorge Bergoglio was born on 17 December in Buenos Aires. He was baptized at the Basilica of San Carlos Borromeo and María Auxiliadora, which belongs to the Salesian congregation.	Bergoglio spent his childhood in the Buenos Aires neighbourhood of Flores with a typical large family of Italian immigrants. He got his love of art from his mother and his love of the San Lorenzo soccer club of Almagro from his father. When he was 13 years old, he finished middle school and got his first job at a sock factory, where he worked as a cleaner.	Bergoglio did his high school studies at a school that specialized in chemistry. When he was 17 years old, he began working in a laboratory. One year later, he finished high school. At the age of 20, he started seminary with the goal of becoming a priest. When he was 21 years old, he suffered a severe case of pneumonia that almost killed him and required the removal of a part of his lung.	In Seminary, Bergoglio studied classic sciences, deepening his knowledge of history, literature, Latin and Greek. From 1964 to 1966, he taught literature and psychology. On 13 December 1969, on the cusp of turning 33 years old, he was ordained as a priest.	In 1973, Bergoglio was named Provincial Superior of the Argentine Jesuits (the order that he belongs to), a post that he would hold until 1979. During the most recent military dictatorship in Argentina (1976–1983), he helped priests who were persecuted for their work in poor communities.

70

1980s	1990s	2000s	2010s
From 1980 to 1986, Bergoglio acted as Rector of the Colegio Máximo de San Miguel in its schools of philosophy and theology. In 1986, he travelled to Germany to complete his doctoral thesis. He later returned to work in the El Salvador school in Buenos Aires.	In 1992, Bergoglio was named Auxiliary Bishop of Buenos Aires. In 1998, after the death of Cardinal Antonio Quarracino, he became Archbishop of Buenos Aires, the most important position in the Argentine Church.	In 2001, Bergoglio was named Cardinal by then Pope John Paul II. During this decade, he acted as Archbishop of Buenos Aires, demonstrating his humility and frugality day after day. He was also committed to important campaigns against drugs and human trafficking. In 2005, after the death of John Paul II, he came in second in the conclave that chose Benedict XVI as his successor.	In February 2013, Benedict XVI announced his resignation as Pope. On 13 March of that same year, Bergoglio was chosen to be the successor of Benedict XVI, the first Latin American and Jesuit Pope. Francis currently represents a possible reorganization of the Church, pushing it closer to the poorest and neediest members of society.

WHO IS FRANCIS?

Pope Francis is the first ever Latin American Pope, and the first non-European since the year 741. He is also the first Pope to belong to the Society of Jesus. Because of this, and because of his constant gestures and dedication to the neediest people in the world, his role as Pope is considered to be a new and exciting step.

Jorge Bergoglio was born on 17 December 1936, in Buenos Aires, the son of Regina María Sívori, a housewife, and Mario José Bergoglio, a railway employee. Jorge grew up in the Flores neighbourhood, in a family of Italian immigrants who had arrived in Argentina in search of a more prosperous future. Following that search, Jorge's parents focused on getting him a good education, as he was the oldest of five children. Given their efforts, he was able to earn the high school title of chemical technician.

The scientific nature of his studies did not keep young Jorge from responding to God's calling. So he prepared to become a priest. He started seminary at the age of 20; two years later, he joined the Society of Jesus. In 1969, after ten years of intense study, he became an ordained priest.

After acting as a teacher and priest for many years, he became Auxiliary Bishop of Buenos Aires. And after the death of Archbishop Quarracino, he came to hold the most important post in the Argentine Church: Archbishop of Buenos Aires and Primate of Argentina. In 2001, he was named Cardinal, and in March 2013, he was elected and named Pope, under the name of Francis.

Despite all of the important positions that he held and continues to hold, he was never blinded by power, nor did he lose sight of his commitment to the poor and the fight for social justice.

FRANCIS AND FILM

Despite the fact that Francis has only been a world-renowned figure for a few years, there are already a few films with him as the main character. They are mainly documentaries that narrate his life and role as Pope. But in 2016, an Argentine biographical miniseries launched, called *Call Me Francis*. The story centres on the last military dictatorship in Argentina and Jorge Bergoglio's efforts to help priests persecuted by the government.

The figure of Saint Francis of Assisi has also been portrayed in films. For example, the classic film *Brother Sun, Sister Moon*, a 1972 British-Italian co-production, dramatizes the life of this poor saint. Major parts of this film were filmed in the town of Assisi.

The work of the Jesuits in America was also the subject of a 1986 film, *The Mission*. It features renowned actors Robert de Niro and Jeremy Irons. This film tells the story of an 18th century Jesuit missionary's efforts to protect a group of native people living in an evangelized community from the Portuguese army. The film is set in the impressive Amazon jungle and at the Iguazú Falls.

HIS THREE INSPIRATIONS

Francis is known for his very diverse education. His specialized high school studies in chemistry blended well with his study of humanities, literature, philosophy and theology, as he studied to become a priest. Similarly, his religious training was also inspired by a number of fields, contributing to his unique personality as Pope.

Saint John Bosco

Francis was baptized as Jorge Bergoglio at the Basilica of San Carlos Borromeo and María Auxiliadora in Buenos Aires. The church was an important hub for the Salesian congregation in Argentina. This congregation was founded by Saint John Bosco (1815–1888) around 1859 in Turin, Italy, and is known for its work with young people, especially those who are poor.

As a young priest from a modest upbringing, Saint John Bosco was able to understand the needs of his time. He made it his goal to gather children who lived on the street and teach them trades that would allow them to make a living for themselves. He also brought communities together to educate them on Christian values. At first, the young priest was considered crazy. But over time, his work was recognized for how it improved the lives of the poor populations.

The Salesian project would soon expand to the rest of the world, and Argentina was the first country outside of Europe where it arrived.

Ignatius of Loyola

Francis is the first Pope from the religious order called the Society of Jesus, whose members are commonly known as "Jesuits". It was founded in 1534 by Ignatius of Loyola (1491–1556). Loyola was a Spanish military man who, after being injured in combat, rediscovered his Catholic faith by reading religious texts. From that moment on, he left his weapons behind and set out for forgiveness for his past life. At the Monastery of Montserrat in Barcelona, he hung his armour in front of the image of the Virgin Mary. He left dressed in rags to continue his pilgrimage. He finally settled in as a hermit in a cave in Manresa. He used this experience to write his book, *Spiritual Exercises*, which would become the foundation for the Society of Jesus.

This order is made up of priests who carry out spiritual, social and educational activities, mostly for the poor. When joining this order, priests take three vows to be poor, celibate and obedient, in tune with Jesus' poor and humble lifestyle. In Latin America, the Jesuits carried out important missionary work among the indigenous people there and also founded schools and universities.

Saint Francis of Assisi

On 13 March 2013, Father Jorge became known around the world as Francis. He is the first Pope to take the name of the poor saint from Assisi, the founder of the Franciscan order, or "the order of friars minor."

Francis of Assisi (1182–1226) was the son of a rich merchant and a noblewoman. In 1202, he became involved in a war between Assisi and Perugia, leading him to spend some time in captivity. From that moment on, he began to feel unsatisfied with his lifestyle and decided to join the ministry to serve the poor. In 1206, he publicly declined his inheritance. He started preaching, with poverty as a fundamental value, and proposed a simple lifestyle based on the ideals of the Gospel.

The following phrase, believed to have been spoken by the saint from Assisi, helps to understand the life of Pope Francis: "My brothers, the Lord called me into the way of simplicity and humility, and this way He has pointed out to me for myself and for those who will believe and follow me..."

GLOSSARY

acolyte person who assists a member of the clergy in a service

arrogant conceited and too proud

baptize pour water on someone as part of a Christian religious practice to welcome a person into the Catholic Church

bishop senior priest in the Catholic Church

catechism summary of religious teachings in the form of questions and answers

chemistry scientific study of substances and their composition

clergy minister, priest or other person appointed to carry out religious work

communion Christian ceremony that honours Jesus' Last Supper, with clergy serving bread and wine

congregation people who meet for worship

dictatorship government ruled by someone who took complete control of a country; dictatorships are usually ruled unjustly

doctrine set of beliefs or rules

frugal someone who lives very carefully so as not to waste anything, especially money

humble not proud

leper used to described someone with a disease that attacks the nerves, skin and muscles

mission church or other place where people work onbehalf of a religious group to spread the group's faith

modest someone who is not boastful about his or her abilities, possessions or achievements ordination act of making someone a Christian priest or minister through a special ceremony

pneumonia serious disease that causes the lungs to become inflamed and filled with a thick fluid that makes breathing difficult

Pope head of the Roman Catholic Church

progressive in favour of improvement, progress and reform, especially in political or social matters

sacrament holy rite in a Christian church, such as baptism, communion, or confession

sacred holy or having to do with religion

sacrifice give up something important or enjoyable for a good reason; to offer something to a god

seminary school where students are trained to become ministers or priests

sexton official of the church who takes care of church buildings and properties

DISCUSSION QUESTIONS

1. What lessons did Jorge learn from working at the laboratory? How do you think this influenced his life in the long run?

2. Why do you think it was hard for Jorge's mum to accept his decision to become a priest? Have you ever been afraid to tell your parents something because of how they would take it?

3. Of his three religious inspirations, which one do you think influenced Pope Francis the most? Why?

WRITING PROMPTS

1. Write a letter to Pope Francis. What would you tell him? Would you ask him for something?

2. Choose a chapter and rewrite it as if it were its own story.

3. Imagine that you are a journalist writing an article about a visit that Pope Francis is making to your city. Imagine the places that he would go and the things that he would do.

ABOUT THE ILLUSTRATOR

Ignacio Segesso, from Buenos Aires, holds a degree in the visual arts. As an artist, he has held collective and individual exhibitions at comic conventions as well as in museums and galleries. He was selected in the Hall of Painting at the Quinquela Martin Museum and in the Contemporary Art Week (SAC) in Mar del Plata. He has worked as a colorist for *Patrulla 666*, which received an award at the 3rd Ibero-American Comics Fair. He won the first Proactiva award, which he received at the UNESCO headquarters in Paris. Currently he participates in the *Anthology of Argentine Heroes* and works on his project *Buenos Aires in Vignettes*, which was honored by the Buenos Aires City Government.

FIND OUT MORE
BOOKS

Dear Pope Francis: The Pope Answers Letters from Children Around the World, Pope Francis (Darton, Longman & Todd, 2016)

Pope Francis: The Story of Our Pope, Ailis Travers (Veritas Publications, 2014)

The Pope, Paul Harrison (Wayland, 2014)

WEBSITES

www.familiam.org/pcpf/s2magazine/index1.jsp?idPagina=11142

Learn more about the Pope's work with children at this website for families.

http://w2.vatican.va/content/vatican/en.html

Visit the Vatican's Holy See website to learn more about Pope Francis and other popes before him.

INDEX